Revision Notes for Intermediate 2
Physics

Lyn Robinson

Principal Teacher of Physics
Williamwood High School, Clarkston

D0333961

Published by
Chemcord
Inch Keith
East Kilbride
Glasgow

ISBN 1 870570 81 2

© Robinson , 2004

Printed by Bell and Bain, Glasgow

Note to student

● **The course**

This book is designed to cover all relevant content statements of the
Intermediate 2 Physics Arrangements.

The course consists of four units:

Mechanic and Heat	1 unit
Electricity and Electronics	1 unit
Waves and Optics	0.5 unit
Radioactivity	0.5 unit

● **Exam structure**

Written Exam Paper   2 hours   100 marks

The marks are approximately equally split between Knowledge and
Understanding and Problem Solving.

There are 20 marks for multiple choice questions.

The Practical Abilities Outcome is assessed within the centre.
You will have to carry out and write up one experiment from one of the
units.

● **Using the book**

You can indicate your knowledge of each statement with a tick in the
❏ at the left hand side.

Space has been left at the right hand side so that you can make
additional notes.

You can also mark statements with a highlighter pen.

● **Exam advice**

Make sure that you have a calculator, protractor, ruler, pen, pencil and
rubber.

Draw a graph lightly in pencil; when you are certain it is correct, go over
in ink.

In numerical questions always put the information into symbol form
and check it is in basic units.

Remember to give units for all answers.

Working through past papers is an essential part of your preparation.

Revision Checklist

	Tick (√) when revised		
	1	**2**	**3**
Unit 1 Mechanics and Heat			
1.1 Kinematics			
1.2 Dynamics			
1.3 Momentum and energy			
1.4 Heat			

Unit 2 Electricity and Electronics			
2.1 Circuits			
2.2 Electrical energy			
2.3 Electromagnetism			
2.4 Electronic components			

Unit 3 Waves and Optics			
3.1 Waves			
3.2 Reflection			
3.3 Refraction			

Unit 4 Radioactivity			
4.1 Ionising radiations			
4.2 Dosimetry			
4.3 Half-life and safety			
4.4 Nuclear reactors			

1.1   KINEMATICS

❏ Speed is how fast an object is travelling and is numerically equal to the distance travelled in one second.

❏ Average speed has the symbol $\overline{v}$, and is measured in metres per second, **m s⁻¹**.

❏ Average speed is given by:

$$\boxed{\overline{v} = \frac{d}{t}}$$

where   **d**   is the distance in m
        t   is the time in s

❏ **Measuring average speed**

The distance is measured out (**d**). The object is then timed from the start to the finish (**t**). The average speed is calculated from the equation:

$$\overline{v} = \frac{d}{t}$$

To increase accuracy, several repeat measurements of time are taken and an average is found.

❏ The instantaneous speed is the speed at one particular point in time and can be very different from the average speed, eg. a car travelling round town may be travelling at 30 m.p.h. at one moment and be stationary at traffic lights a few minutes later. Its average speed could be 12 m.p.h. which is different from the instantaneous speeds.

❏ **Measuring the instantaneous speed**

The time interval must be as short as possible. A light gate connected to an electronic timer will achieve this. When a card attached to the moving object breaks a light beam in the light gate, the timer starts. As soon as the beam is remade the timer stops. The speed can be calculated by:

$$\text{speed} = \frac{\text{length of card}}{\text{time beam is broken}}$$

❏ The shorter the time interval, the closer this average speed comes to the instantaneous speed.

❏ Any method of measuring time which involves a stop watch is inaccurate because of the reaction time of the person using the stopwatch.

❑ A **scalar quantity** has a magnitude (size) only.
A **vector quantity** has both magnitude and direction.

❑ When stating a vector quantity both magnitude and direction must be given.

❑ Both distance, **d**, and displacement, **s**, are measured in metres, but distance is a scalar quantity and displacement is a vector quantity, eg. displacement can be described as the distance travelled in a particular direction from the starting point.

❑ The distance and displacement for the same journey can be very different. Consider, for example, a runner on a 400 m circular track. At the end of the race he has covered a distance of 400 m but as he has arrived back at his starting point his final displacement is zero.

❑ Both speed and velocity have the symbol **v** and are measured in metres per second, **m s^{-1}**.

❑ Speed is a scalar quantity and has magnitude only and can be described as the distance covered in unit time.

❑ Velocity is a vector quantity and has both magnitude and direction. It can be described as the speed in a particular direction and is equal to the displacement per unit time.

❑

$$\text{speed} = \frac{\text{distance}}{\text{time}} \qquad \text{velocity} = \frac{\text{displacement}}{\text{time}}$$

❑ All variables can be classified as vector or scalar quantities:

Scalar	Vector
distance	displacement
speed	velocity
time	acceleration
mass	force
energy	momentum
power	weight

❑ Acceleration is the change in velocity in unit time. It has the symbol **a**, and is usually measured in metres per second per second, **m s^{-2}**.

❑ Acceleration is given by:

$$a = \frac{v - u}{t}$$

where u is the initial speed in m s^{-1}
v is the final speed in m s^{-1}
t is the time in s

❑ If the two speeds are given in m.p.h. and the time in seconds, then the acceleration will be in miles per hour per second.

❑ *Example*
What is the acceleration of a trolley which starts at 6.5 m s^{-1} and is travelling at 50 cm s^{-1} after 3 s?

Step 1 Put the information into symbol form and change to basic units.

u = 6.5 m s^{-1}
v = 50 cm s^{-1} = 0.5 m s^{-1}
t = 3 s

Step 2 Choose the correct equation.

$$a = \frac{v - u}{t}$$

Step 3 Put the numbers into the equation and calculate the answer.

$$a = \frac{v - u}{t} = \frac{0.5 - 6.5}{3} = \frac{-6}{3} = -2 \text{ m s}^{-2}$$

DO NOT FORGET UNITS.

❑ The negative sign shows that this is a deceleration, ie. the trolley is slowing down.

❑ The acceleration formula can be rewritten:

$$v = u + at$$

❑ *Example*

If a trolley accelerates from rest at 50 cm s⁻² for
15 s, what is the final speed?

Step 1   Put the information into symbol form and
change to basic units.

u = 0
a = 50 cm s⁻² = 0.5 m s⁻²
t = 15 s

Step 2   Choose the correct equation.

$v = u + at$

Step 3   Put the numbers into the equation and
calculate the answer.

$v = u + at$
= 0 + 0.5 × 15 = 7.5 m s⁻¹

DO NOT FORGET UNITS.

Velocity - time graphs

❑ Steady velocity

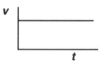

❑ Speeding up
(Accelerating)

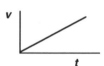

❑ Slowing Down
(Decelerating)

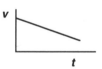

The information from a velocity - time graph can be
used to calculate:

the **acceleration** using $a = \dfrac{v - u}{t}$

the **distance travelled** which is equal to the **area** under
a velocity - time graph

❑ The **maximum acceleration** is found by calculating all
accelerations and choosing the largest, or using the line
with the steepest gradient.

❑ If the object is moving in a straight line in one direction,
then the distance travelled is equivalent to the
displacement.

❏ **Example 1**
Use the following graph to
(a) describe the motion,
(b) calculate all accelerations,
(c) calculate the distance travelled (displacement).

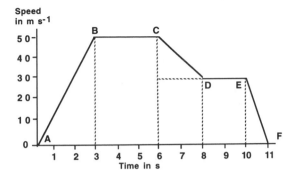

(a) AB - accelerating from rest to 50 m s⁻¹ in 3 s

    BC - constant speed of 50 m s⁻¹ for 3 s

    CD - decelerating from 50 m s⁻¹ to 30 m s⁻¹ in 2 s

    DE - constant speed of 30 m s⁻¹ for 2 s

    EF - decelerating from 30 m s⁻¹ to rest in 1 s

(b) AB $a = \dfrac{v - u}{t} = \dfrac{50 - 0}{3} = $ **16.7 m s⁻²**

CD $a = \dfrac{v - u}{t} = \dfrac{30 - 50}{2} = $ **- 10 m s⁻²**

EF $a = \dfrac{v - u}{t} = \dfrac{0 - 30}{1} = $ **- 30 m s⁻²**

(c) Distance travelled = area under the graph

AB $ = \frac{1}{2}(3 \times 50)$ = 75 m

BC $ = (3 \times 50)$ = 150 m

CD $ = \frac{1}{2}[(50 - 30) \times 2] + 2 \times 30 = 20 + 60$ = 80 m

DE $ = (2 \times 30)$ = 60 m

EF $ = \frac{1}{2}(30 \times 1)$ = 15 m

                        Total distance   = **380 m**

Since this object is moving in one direction, in a straight line, the displacement is also 380 m.

❑ *Example 2*

Use the following graph to

(a) describe the motion,

(b) calculate the distance travelled.

(c) calculate the final displacement.

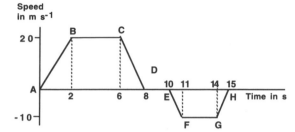

(a) AB - accelerating from rest to 20 m s⁻¹ in 2 s

BC - constant speed of 20 m s⁻¹ for 4 s

CD - decelerating from 20 m s⁻¹ to rest in 2 s

DE - at rest for 2 s

EF - accelerating from rest to -10 m s⁻¹ in the opposite direction for 1 s

FG - constant speed of -10 m s⁻¹ for 3 s in the opposite direction

GH - decelerating to rest from -10 m s⁻¹ in 1 s

(b) Distance travelled = area under the graph

$$AB = \tfrac{1}{2}(2 \times 20) = 20 \text{ m}$$

$$BC = (4 \times 20) = 80 \text{ m}$$

$$CD = \tfrac{1}{2}(2 \times 20) = 20 \text{ m}$$

$$EF = \tfrac{1}{2}(1 \times 10) = 5 \text{ m}$$

$$FG = (3 \times 10) = 30 \text{ m}$$

$$GH = \tfrac{1}{2}(1 \times 10) = 5 \text{ m}$$

Total distance = **160 m**

(c) Displacement = area above *t* axis - area below *t* axis

s = area ABCD - area EFGH

s = 120 - 40 = **80 m** in the original direction

1.2   DYNAMICS

❑   Force has the symbol **F**, and is measured in newtons, **N**.

❑   A force can change:

(1) the shape of an object,
(2) the speed of an object,
(3) the direction in which an object is moving.

❑   A **Newton balance** (or spring balance) is used to measure force.

❑   The Newton balance contains a spring. The spring becomes longer when a force is applied to the balance. The increase in length is directly proportional to the force.

❑   **Weight** is a force and is measured in newtons.

❑   The weight of an object is the Earth's pull on the object.

❑   The **mass** of an object is the amount of matter in the object.

❑   The mass of an object does not change but the weight depends on the gravitational field strength and can vary.

❑   The weight per unit mass is called the **gravitational field strength**. It has the symbol **g**, and is measured in newtons per kilogram, **N kg⁻¹**.

$$g = \frac{W}{m}$$

where **W** is the weight in N
m is the mass in kg

❑   The approximate value of **g** is **10 N kg⁻¹** on Earth.

❑   The acceleration due to gravity is numerically equal to the gravitational field strength, eg. on Earth, **g** $= 10$ N kg⁻¹ and the acceleration due to gravity is 10 m s⁻².

❑   The relationship between gravitational field strength, weight and mass can be rewritten:

$$W = mg$$

❑ *Example*

(a) What is the weight of a 70 kg man on Earth?

(b) What is his mass on Mars?

(c) What is his weight on Mars? ($g = 3.7$ N kg^{-1})

Step 1 Put the information into symbol form.

$$m = 70 \text{ kg}$$
$$g_{\text{Earth}} = 10 \text{ N kg}^{-1}$$
$$g_{\text{Mars}} = 3.7 \text{ N kg}^{-1}$$

Step 2 Choose the correct equation.

$$W = mg$$

Step 3 Put the numbers into the equation and calculate the answer.

(a) $W_{\text{Earth}} = mg = 70 \times 10 = \textbf{700 N}$

(b) Mass is constant => mass on Mars = **70 kg**

(c) $W_{\text{Mars}} = mg = 70 \times 3.7 = \textbf{259 N}$

DO NOT FORGET UNITS.

❑ **Friction** is a force which opposes the motion of a body.

❑ Friction is **increased** by:

(1) applying brakes,

(2) opening a parachute; there is more air resistance so that the person falls more slowly,

(3) using aerofoils on racing cars; the aerofoils hold the car down and allow faster cornering.

❑ Friction is **decreased** by:

(1) using oil between moving parts in machinery,

(2) making objects streamlined; there is less resistance,

(3) reducing the area of contact, eg. using wheels or rollers,

(4) making surfaces smooth, eg. wax on skis.

❏ Force is a vector quantity.

❏ The direction of a force is important.

❏ If the forces acting in opposite directions are equal, they are called **balanced forces**, eg.

❏ Balanced forces have the same effect on motion as having no force at all.

❏ When the forces are balanced or there are no forces, the velocity remains constant.

❏ When an object is moving at a constant velocity, the forces on it are either balanced or zero.

❏ **Newton's First Law** states that an object remains at rest or continues with a constant velocity, unless there is an unbalanced force acting.

❏ The motion of a spaceship is consistent with Newton's First Law. Space is a vacuum so there are no frictional forces acting. The ship continues moving at the same speed in the same direction until it comes under the gravitational influence of a planet.

❏ Seat belts are used in cars to provide a backwards force to prevent the passenger continuing to move forward if the car stops suddenly. If there was no such force, from Newton's First Law, the passenger would continue moving forward and may go through the windscreen.

❏ When the force stays the same and the mass increases, the acceleration decreases.

❏ When the mass stays the same and the force increases, the acceleration increases.

❑ **Newton's Second Law** is:

$$F = ma$$

where F is the force in N
m is the mass in kg
a is the acc. in m s^{-2}

❑ The resultant of a number of forces acting on an object is the single force which will produce the same effect on the object.

❑ The unbalanced or resultant force must be used for F in the above equation.

❑ Force is measured in newtons, N, where:
"1 newton is the resultant (or unbalanced) force which causes a mass of 1 kg to accelerate at 1 m s^{-2}."

❑ Problems involving several forces and objects can be solved by:

(1) In all situations apply:
Unbalanced force = mass x acceleration

(2) Draw a sketch diagram for the complete system. This must include all masses and any external forces. Do not forget forces due to gravity.

(3) If appropriate apply $F = ma$ to the whole system.

(4) If only part of the system is to be considered, select the object involved and draw a 'free-body' diagram for that object, ie. draw a sketch with all the forces exerted on this object, both external and by other parts of the system.

(5) Indicate on the free-body diagram the direction of the acceleration of this object.

(6) Apply $F = ma$ to the individual body.

❑ *Example 1*
What is the mass of an object if an unbalanced force of 20 N produces an acceleration of 4 m s^{-2}?

Step 1 Put the information into symbol form.
$F = 20$ N
$a = 4$ m s^{-2}

Step 2 Choose the correct equation.
$$F = ma \implies m = \frac{F}{a}$$

Step 3 Put the numbers into the equation and calculate the answer.
$$m = \frac{F}{a} = \frac{20}{4} = 5 \text{ kg}$$

DO NOT FORGET UNITS.

❑ *Example 2*

What is the acceleration of a 600 kg car, when the
engine exerts a force of 1700 N, but the frictional force is
800 N?

Step 1   Draw a simple diagram showing the forces
acting and their directions.

800 N ◀━━ | 600 kg | ━━▶ 1700 N

Step 2   Calculate the resultant (unbalanced) force.

F = 1700 - 800 = 900 N

| 600 kg | ━━▶ 900 N

Step 3   Put the information into symbol form and
change to basic units.

F = 900 N
m = 600 kg

Step 4   Choose the correct equation.

$$F = ma \quad => \quad a = \frac{F}{m}$$

Step 5   Put the numbers into the equation and
calculate the answer.

$$a = \frac{F}{m} = \frac{900}{600} = 1.5 \text{ m s}^{-2}$$

DO NOT FORGET UNITS.

❑   The two equations:

$$a = \frac{F}{m} \qquad \text{and} \qquad a = \frac{v - u}{t}$$

can be used to calculate the acceleration.

NOTE :   *Choose the correct equation for the information
given. Often both equations are used in same
question.*

❏ *Example 3*

What is the acceleration of a 700 kg helicopter, when the engine exerts a force of 9800 N vertically upwards, but the frictional force is 800 N?

Step 1 Draw a simple diagram showing the forces acting and their directions.
Remember the forces due to gravity.

$$W = mg = 700 \times 10 = 7000 \text{ N}$$

$$\uparrow 9800 \text{ N}$$

$$\boxed{700 \text{ kg}}$$

$$800 \text{ N} \downarrow \quad \downarrow W = 7000 \text{ N}$$

Step 2 Calculate the resultant (unbalanced) force.

$$F = 9800 - (800 + 7000) = 2000 \text{ N}$$

$$\uparrow 2000 \text{ N}$$

$$\boxed{700 \text{ kg}}$$

Step 3 Put the information into symbol form and change to basic units.

$$F = 2000 \text{ N}$$
$$m = 700 \text{ kg}$$

Step 4 Choose the correct equation.

$$F = ma \implies a = \frac{F}{m}$$

Step 5 Put the numbers into the equation and calculate the answer.

$$a = \frac{F}{m} = \frac{2000}{700} = 2.9 \text{ m s}^{-2}$$

DO NOT FORGET UNITS.

❑ The overall effect due to a number of vectors is called the **resultant,** eg. several forces in varying directions will give a final resultant force.

❑ The direction of the individual vectors must be taken into account when calculating the resultant by scale diagram or by calculation.

❑ The resultant of two vectors, A_1 and A_2, can be found by drawing a **vector triangle**. The vectors are added 'nose to tail', ie. the second vector, A_2, is drawn starting where the first vector, A_1, finishes:

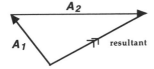

Each vector has to be drawn in the correct direction and to a suitable scale. The resultant is the line joining the first unconnected tail to the last unconnected head. The magnitude of the resultant is found by measuring the length and using the scale in reverse. The direction is given by measuring a suitable angle from the diagram.

❑ If the two vectors are at right angles then Pythagoras' theorem can be used to calculate the resultant:

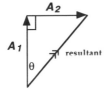

❑ The magnitude of the resultant vector is given by:

$$\text{Resultant} = \sqrt{(A_1)^2 + (A_2)^2}$$

❑ Direction is given by calculating θ:

$$\tan \theta = \frac{A_2}{A_1}$$

❑ Both magnitude and direction **must** be given when quoting a vector answer.

❏ *Example*

What is the resultant force on a model aircraft if there are two forces acting 120 N north and then 90 N east?

Step 1   Draw a sketch diagram of the situation.

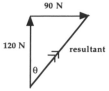

Step 2   Decide from the sketch whether the problem can best be solved by calculation or if a scale diagram is required.

In this case, since the two vector quantities are at right angles, the resultant can be found using Pythagoras' theorem:

$$\text{Resultant} \ = \ \sqrt{120^2 + 90^2} \ = \ 22\,500 \ = \ 150 \text{ N}$$

Since force is a vector quantity the direction must be calculated as well:

$$\tan \theta \ = \ \frac{90}{120} \ => \ \theta = 36.9°$$

The resultant force is **150 N at 36.9° east of north.**

NOTE :   *In this case the right angled triangle is an example of a 3, 4, 5 triangle (3 x 30 N, 4 x 3 N, 5 x 30 N); this is often the case and gives a quick way of obtaining the answer.*

NOTE :   *Answers obtained by scale diagrams are normally less accurate than those found by calculation.*

❏ Acceleration due to gravity, g, is 10 m s^{-2} on Earth. The gravitational field strength is 10 N kg^{-1} on Earth. Both have the same numerical value but the units are different. This is always true for all planets.

❏ The acceleration due to gravity and the gravitational field strength are equivalent.

Force due to gravity $\quad \textbf{\textit{W}} \ = \ \textbf{\textit{m g}}$

Gravitational field strength $\ = \ \dfrac{\text{force due to gravity}}{\text{mass}}$

$$= \ \dfrac{\textbf{\textit{W}}}{\textbf{\textit{m}}}$$

$$= \ \dfrac{\textbf{\textit{mg}}}{\textbf{\textit{m}}}$$

$$= \ \textbf{\textit{g}}$$

❏ A projectile projected horizontally will follow a curved path as shown:

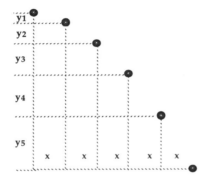

❏ **Horizontally** the distance, **x**, travelled in a fixed time, is always constant. Therefore **the horizontal speed is constant.** This is true because there are no forces acting horizontally (provided air resistance is negligible).

❏ **Vertically**, the distance, **y**, travelled in a fixed time, increases because gravity is acting on the object and therefore the vertical speed increases.
The vertical acceleration is constant (10 m s^{-2}).

❏ Horizontal and vertical motion are **independent**. Only time is common.

❑ *Example*

An aircraft travelling horizontally at 200 m s^{-1} drops a package which hits the ground 6 s later.

Ignoring air resistance, find

(a) how fast package is going vertically just as it lands,
(b) how fast it is going horizontally just as it lands,
(c) the height of the aircraft,
(d) how far the package travels horizontally (range),
(e) where the plane is, compared to the package, when the package lands.

Step 1   Divide the page into two halves and put the information into symbol form.

Vertical

t = 6 s

u_v = 0 (as it leaves plane)

a_v = 10 m s^{-2} (gravity)

Horizontal

t = 6 s

u_h = 200 m s^{-1} (same as plane)

a_h = 0

NOTE : *u_v, a_v and a_h are not given but are true from properties of projectiles.*

Step 2   Choose the correct equations. Put in the numbers and calculate the answers.

(a) v = $u + a t$
     v_v = 0 + 10 × 6
        = **60 m s^{-1}**

(b) $u_h = v_h$ = **200 m s^{-1}**
     (horizontal speed constant)

NOTE : *To find the distances, sketch velocity - time graphs. The distances are the areas under the graphs.*

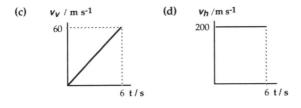

(c) v_v / m s^{-1}

60

6 t / s

(d) v_h / m s^{-1}

200

6 t / s

d_v = $\frac{1}{2}(60 \times 6)$
    = **180 m**

d_h = 200 × 6
    = **1200 m**

(e) The package is travelling horizontally at the same speed as the plane.
If the plane does not change direction or speed, after 6 s it will be 180 m vertically above the package.

1.3 MOMENTUM AND ENERGY

❏ A rocket is pushed forward because the 'propellant' is pushed back.

❏ **A** pushes **B** and **B** pushes **A** back,
eg. bat pushes ball and ball pushes back on bat.

❏ **Newton's Third Law** states that:
" If **A** exerts a force on **B**, **B** exerts an equal and opposite force on **A**".

❏ **A** and **B** are known as "Newton pairs",
eg.

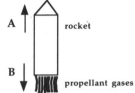

A is the force of propellant gases on the rocket.
B is the force of the rocket on propellant gases.

❏ In each case the nouns change position,
eg.

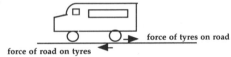

❏ "Newton pairs" always act on different objects, eg. on the road and on the tyres.

❏ There may be many Newton pairs of forces acting,
eg.

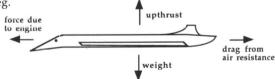

Here the Newton pairs are:

Weight
force of Earth on plane = force of plane on Earth

Upthrust
force of displaced air on plane = force of plane on displaced air

Drag
frictional force of air on plane = force of plane on air

Engine
force of plane on expelled gases = force of gases on plane

❑ Do not confuse **balanced** forces which act on the **same object** and **Newton pairs** which always act on **different objects**.

❑ **Momentum** sometimes has the symbol p, and is measured in kilogram metres per second, **kg m s^{-1}**.

❑ Momentum is defined as mass multiplied by velocity:

$$\text{momentum} = m\,v$$

❑ Momentum is a vector quantity and for motion in a straight line one convention is:
an object travelling right $\longrightarrow$ has positive momentum
an object travelling left $\longleftarrow$ has negative momentum

❑ There are two types of interaction between bodies, collisions and explosions.

❑ Momentum is conserved in both types of interaction, ie. **total momentum before = total momentum after**

❑ The Principle of Conservation of Linear Momentum states that:
"For any interaction between two objects moving along the same straight line, momentum is conserved, provided there are no external forces acting on the objects."

❑ *Example*

What is the final velocity of a 4 kg block, initially at rest, which is hit from behind by a 7 kg block moving at 9 m s^{-1}? The 7 kg block is slowed down to 5 m s^{-1} by the collision.

Step 1 Draw a diagram of the before and after situations with all relevant masses and velocities.

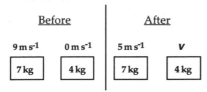

Before | After

9 m s^{-1} 0 m s^{-1} | 5 m s^{-1} v

7 kg   4 kg | 7 kg   4 kg

NOTE : *It is essential to draw this diagram accurately as there are a number of masses and velocities and it is very easy to be confused.*

Step 2 Calculate the total momentum before and after.

Before	After
momentum = $m\,v$	momentum = $m\,v$
$\text{mom}_{\text{before}} = (7 \times 9) + (4 \times 0)$	$\text{mom}_{\text{after}} = (7 \times 5) + 4v$
$= 63 + 0$	$= 35 + 4v$
$= 63 \text{ kg m s}^{-1}$	

Step 3 Calculate v by equating $\text{mom}_{\text{before}}$ and $\text{mom}_{\text{after}}$ since total momentum is conserved during all collisions.

$$63 = 35 + 4v$$
$$28 = 4\,v$$
$$7 \text{ m s}^{-1} = v$$

The 4 kg block moves in the original direction of the 7 kg block (since v is positive), at 7 m s^{-1}.

❑ Energy can be changed from one form into another (energy transformations) but it cannot be created or destroyed.
Energy is always conserved.

❑ All forms of energy can be measured in joules, J.

❑ In many energy transformations energy is 'lost' as heat due to friction.

❑ The **work done** is a measure of the energy transferred. Work done has the symbol E_W, and is measured in joules, J.

❑ Work done is related to force and distance by the equation:

$$E_W = F\,d$$

where F is the force in N
d is the distance in m

❑ *Example*
How far must a 5 N force have pulled a 50 g toy car if 30 J of energy are transferred?

Step 1 Put the information into symbol form and change to basic units.

F = 5 N
m = 50 g = 0.05 kg
E = 30 J

NOTE : *The mass is extra unnecessary information.*

Step 2 Choose the correct equation.

$$E_W = F\,d \quad \Rightarrow \quad d = \frac{E_W}{F}$$

Step 3 Put the numbers into the equation and calculate the answer.

$$d = \frac{E_W}{F} = \frac{30}{5} = 6\,\text{m}$$

DO NOT FORGET UNITS.

NOTE : *You do not always need to use all the information given.*

❑ **Power** has the symbol P, and is measured in watts, **W**.
One watt is one joule per second:
$$1 \text{ W} = 1 \text{ J s}^{-1}$$

❑ Power is related to energy and time by the equation:

$$\boxed{P = \frac{E}{t}}$$ where E is the energy in J
t is the time in s

❑ This general equation is true when the energy involved is work done, ie. $E = E_W$.

❑ *Example*

What is the power of a cyclist who exerts a force of 50 N and moves 3 km in 10 minutes?

Step 1 Put the information into symbol form and change to basic units.

$F = 50 \text{ N}$
$d = 3 \text{ km} = 3000 \text{ m}$
$t = 10 \text{ mins} = 600 \text{ s}$

Step 2 Choose the correct equations.

$E_W = F d$
$P = \dfrac{E}{t}$

Step 3 Put the numbers into the equations and calculate the answer.

$E_W = F d = 50 \times 3000 = 150\,000 \text{ J}$
$P = \dfrac{E}{t} = \dfrac{150\,000}{600} = 250 \text{ W}$

DO NOT FORGET UNITS.

NOTE : *In this case two equations have to be used to find the answer.*

❑ The work done against gravity is the **gravitational potential energy**. It has the symbol E_p and is measured in joules, J.

❑ $$E_p = m g h$$

where m is the mass in kg
g is the acceleration due to gravity, 10 m s^{-2}
h is the vertical height in m

❑ The change in gravitational potential energy is the work done against or by gravity.

- **Kinetic energy** is the energy an object has because it is moving. It has the symbol E_k, and is measured in joules, **J**.

- When the mass of the moving object is increased E_k increases.

- When the speed of the moving object is increased E_k increases.

- $$E_k = \frac{1}{2} m v^2$$ where E_k is the kinetic energy in J
            m is the mass in kg
            v is the speed in m s^{-1}

- To find the speed given the kinetic energy and the mass, use the equation:

$$v = \sqrt{\frac{2 E_k}{m}}$$

- *Example*
  What is the kinetic energy of a 3 kg trolley moving at 80 cm s^{-1}?

  Step 1   Put the information into symbol form and change to basic units.

       $m = 3 \, \text{kg}$
       $v = 80 \, \text{cm s}^{-1} = 0.8 \, \text{m s}^{-1}$

  Step 2   Choose the correct equation.

       $E_k = \frac{1}{2} m v^2$

  Step 3   Put the numbers into the equation and calculate the answer.

       $E_k = \frac{1}{2} m v^2 = \frac{1}{2} \times 3 \times (0.8)^2 = 0.96 \, \text{J}$

DO NOT FORGET UNITS.

NOTE :   *When using this equation it is only the speed which is squared.*

❑ Since energy is conserved, if it is possible to calculate the total energy at any one point, then the total energy is known at every other point.

❑ *Example*
A 250 g pendulum bob is raised 20 cm from its rest position and released.
(a) What is the potential energy at **A**?
(b) What is the kinetic energy at **B**?
(c) How fast is it travelling at **B**?

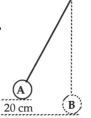

20 cm   B

Step 1 Put the information into symbol form and change to basic units.

$$m \;=\; 250 \text{ g} \;=\; 0.25 \text{ kg}$$
$$h \;=\; 20 \text{ cm} \;=\; 0.2 \text{ m}$$
$$g \;=\; 10 \text{ m s}^{-2}$$

(a) Step 2 Choose the correct equation.

$$E_p = m\,g\,h$$

Step 3 Put the numbers into the equation and calculate the answer.

$$E_p = m\,g\,h = 0.25 \times 10 \times 0.2 = 0.5 \text{ J}$$

(b) $E_k = E_p$ since energy is conserved.

$$E_k = 0.5 \text{ J}$$

(c) Step 2 Choose the correct equation.

$$E_k = \tfrac{1}{2}\,m\,v^2 \quad => \quad v = \sqrt{\frac{2\,E_k}{m}}$$

Step 3 Put the numbers into the equation and calculate the answer.

$$v = \sqrt{\frac{2\,E_k}{m}} = \sqrt{\frac{2 \times 0.5}{0.25}}$$

$$= \sqrt{4}$$

$$= 2 \text{ m s}^{-1}$$

DO NOT FORGET UNITS.

❑ Since the formulae for both E_k and E_p contain the mass, the speed or the height can be calculated, given the other, without needing to know the mass:

$$E_p = E_k$$
$$mgh = \tfrac{1}{2}mv^2$$

The mass can be cancelled from both sides:

$$gh = \tfrac{1}{2}v^2$$

This can be written as:

$$v = \sqrt{2gh}$$

❑ *Example*
A man kicks a ball off a cliff which is 125 m high.
(a) How fast is it travelling vertically just before it hits the ground?
(b) What assumption is being made to obtain the answer?

(a) **Step 1** Put the information into symbol form.

$$h = 125 \text{ m}$$
$$g = 10 \text{ m s}^{-2}$$

NOTE : *This is not stated in the question but is always true for vertical movement.*

Step 2 Choose the correct equation.

$$v = \sqrt{2gh}$$

Step 3 Put the numbers into the equation and calculate the answer.

$$v = \sqrt{2gh} = \sqrt{2 \times 10 \times 125}$$
$$= 50 \text{ m s}^{-1}$$

DO NOT FORGET UNITS.

(b) The assumption made is that no energy is lost. All the potential energy becomes kinetic energy.

❑ In practice, some energy is always 'lost' as heat. The value obtained for the speed is therefore a maximum possible value.

❑   When energy is changed from one form into another, the efficiency of the system is given by:

$$\text{efficiency} = \frac{\text{energy out}}{\text{energy in}} \times 100\,\%$$

or

$$\text{efficiency} = \frac{\text{power out}}{\text{power in}} \times 100\,\%$$

❑   *Example*

A 2 kW electric motor takes 15 seconds to raise a 65 kg box onto a ledge 12 m up a cliff.
Calculate the efficiency of the operation.

Step 1   Put the information into symbol form.

h = 12 m
g = 10 m s^{-2}
m = 65 kg
P = 2 kW = 2000 W
t = 15 s

Step 2   Choose the correct equations.

E_p = mgh (energy out)
E = Pt (energy in)

$$\text{efficiency} = \frac{\text{energy out}}{\text{energy in}} \times 100\,\%$$

Step 3   Put the numbers into the equation and calculate the answer.

E_{out} = E_p = 65 × 10 × 12 = 7800 J

E_{in} = 2000 × 15 = 30 000 J

$$\text{efficiency} = \frac{7800}{30\,000} \times 100 = \mathbf{26\,\%}$$

DO NOT FORGET UNITS.

NOTE :   *Efficiency is never more than 100 %, this would mean energy is created. Take care to identify the energy in and the energy out correctly. If your answer comes out larger than 100 % it usually means you have confused energy in and energy out.*

1.4 HEAT

❑ **Temperature** is a measure of how hot or cold something is. It is measured in degrees Celsius, °C.

❑ **Heat** is a form of energy and is measured in joules, J.

❑ If a substance gains heat then its temperature can increase.

❑ For different substances, it takes varying amounts of energy to raise the temperature of 1 kg by 1 °C. The amount of energy required is called the **specific heat capacity** of the substance. This has the symbol c and is measured in joules per kilogram per degree Celsius, J kg⁻¹ °C⁻¹.

❑ When a substance is heated up, without changing state, the heat energy required is:

$$\boxed{E_h = c\, m\, \Delta T}$$

where E_h is the heat in J

c is the specific heat capacity in J kg⁻¹ °C⁻¹

m is the mass in kg

ΔT is the **change** in temperature in °C

❑ *Example*
What is the final temperature when 150 kJ of energy is given to 2 kg of water at 20 °C?

Step 1   Put information into symbol form and change to basic units.

E_h = 150 kJ = 150 000 J

m = 2 kg

c_{water} = 4200 J kg⁻¹ °C⁻¹ (find from data tables)

T_{initial} = 20 °C

Step 2   Choose the correct equation.

$$E_h = c\, m\, \Delta T \quad => \quad \Delta T = \frac{E_h}{c\, m}$$

Step 3   Put the numbers into the equation and calculate the answer.

$$\Delta T = \frac{E_h}{c\, m} = \frac{150\ 000}{4200 \times 2} = 17.9\ °C$$

Final temperature = T_{initial} + ΔT = 20 + 17.9 = **37.9 °C**

❑ Heat can be produced from many other forms of energy, eg. electrical, kinetic, or potential.
Since energy is conserved, the amount of heat energy can be found by calculating the other form.

❑ Useful equations are:

$$E = P\,t \qquad E_e = I\,V\,t \qquad E_k = \tfrac{1}{2}\,m\,v^2$$

$$E_p = m\,g\,h \qquad E_w = F\,d$$

Any of these can then be put equal to $c\,m\,\Delta T$ as energy is conserved (provided no energy is 'lost', ie. the system is 100 % efficient).

❑ The three states of matter are solid, liquid and gas.

❑ Heat is gained or lost by a substance when its state is changed.

❑ When a substance changes state, its temperature remains the same until the change of state is complete.

❑ The **changes of state** are :

Evaporation	-	liquid to gas
Condensation	-	gas to liquid
Freezing	-	liquid to solid
Melting	-	solid to liquid

❑   **Melting**   **Evaporation**

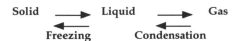

Solid ⟶ **Liquid** ⟶ **Gas**

    Freezing   **Condensation**

For either change ⟶ energy must be provided;

for either change ⟵ energy is given out.

❑ The amount of energy needed to change state depends only on the mass of the substance and what it is.

❑ To change 1 kg of a substance from solid to liquid (or liquid to solid) involves energy equal to the **specific latent heat of fusion, L$_{fusion}$**. This is different for each substance.

❑ To change 1 kg of a substance from liquid to gas (or gas to liquid) involves energy equal to the **specific latent heat of vaporisation, L$_{vaporisation}$**. This is different for each substance.

❑ The specific latent heat of vaporisation is always larger than the specific latent heat of fusion. It takes more energy for molecules to break right away from the rest in the liquid and form a gas, than it does to break the bonds holding molecules in the solid, in order to form a liquid.

❑ When a substance changes state, the heat energy required is:

$$E_h = m\,L$$

where E_h is the heat in J
m is the mass in kg
L is the specific latent heat in J kg^{-1}

❑ The above equation is true for all changes of state as long as the correct latent heat is used.

❑ *Example*
How much energy is required to change 3 kg of water at 20 °C all into steam at 100 °C?

Step 1 Put information into symbol form and change to basic units.

m = 3 kg
T initial = 20 °C
T final = 100 °C,   therefore ΔT = 80 °C
c water = 4200 J k^{-1} °C^{-1}
L vaporisation for water = 2.26 x 10^6 J kg^{-1}

Step 2 Choose the correct equations.

$E_h = c\,m\,\Delta T$
$E_h = m\,L$

Step 3 Put the numbers into the equations and calculate the answers.

(1) to raise to boiling
$E_h = c\,m\,\Delta T$ = 4200 x 3 x 80 = 1 008 000 J

(2) to turn into gas
$E_h = m\,L$ = 3 x 2.26 x 10^6 = 6 780 000 J

Total energy = 1 008 000 + 6 780 000 = **7 788 000 J**

DO NOT FORGET UNITS.

NOTE : *This type of question must be done in two parts.*
(i) Calculate the energy needed to bring water to boiling.
(ii) Calculate the energy to turn the water into steam.

UNIT 2   ELECTRICITY AND ELECTRONICS

2.1   CIRCUITS

❑   An electric current is caused by the movement of charges (negative electrons) round a circuit.

❑   **Conductors**, eg. metals such as copper and silver, have many electrons that are 'free' to move. Conductors allow a current to flow through them.

❑   **Insulators**, eg. rubber and plastic, have very few 'free' electrons and therefore do not allow a current to flow.

❑   Current has the symbol I, and is measured in amperes (amps), **A**.

❑   Charge has the symbol Q, and is measured in coulombs, **C**.

❑   The voltage of a supply is a measure of the energy given to the charges in a circuit, eg. a 1.5 V battery gives 1.5 J of energy to each coulomb of charge passing through it.

❑   Charge, current and time are related by the equation:

$$Q = I\,t$$

where Q is the charge in C
　　　　 I is the current in A
　　　　 t is the time in s

❑   *Example*
What is the current when 600 C of charge is transferred in 5 minutes?

Step 1   Put the information into symbol form and change to basic units.

Q = 600 C
t = 5 mins = 5 × 60 = 300 s

Step 2   Choose the correct equation.

$$Q = I\,t \quad \Rightarrow \quad I = \frac{Q}{t}$$

Step 3   Put the numbers into the equation and calculate the answer.

$$I = \frac{Q}{t} = \frac{600}{300} = 2 \text{ A}$$

DO NOT FORGET UNITS.

Circuit symbols

- cell

- battery

- fuse

- lamp

- resistor

- variable resistor

- capacitor

- diode

- switch

- Voltage has the symbol **V**, and is measured in volts, **V**.

- The voltage of a supply is a measure of the energy given to the charges in the circuit.

- Current is measured by an ammeter; voltage is measured by a voltmeter.

- The circuit symbols for an ammeter and a voltmeter are:

- An ammeter is always placed in series in the circuit.

- A voltmeter is always placed in parallel.

❏ **Circuit diagram**

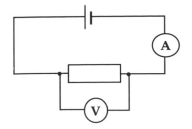

❏ There is only one path round a **series circuit**:

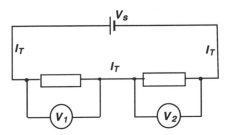

❏ The current is the same at all points in the series circuit.

❏ The supply voltage is equal to the sum of the voltages (potential differences) across the various components in a series circuit:

$$V_s = V_1 + V_2$$

❏ There is more than one path round a **parallel circuit**. The various paths are known as branches.

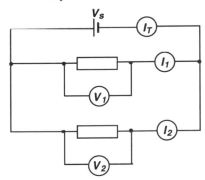

❏ The potential difference (voltage) across components in parallel is the same for each component.

$$V_s = V_1 = V_2$$

- The sum of the currents in parallel branches is equal to the current drawn from the supply:

$$I_T = I_1 + I_2$$

- Resistance has to do with the difficulty charges have in moving; it has the symbol R, and is measured in ohms, Ω.

- When the resistance in the circuit increases, the current in the circuit decreases.

- For a given resistor $\dfrac{V}{I}$ is approximately constant even when the current changes.
  $\dfrac{V}{I}$ is called the resistance of the resistor.

- **Ohm's law**

$$V = I R$$

where V is the voltage in V
I is the current in A
R is the resistance in Ω

- *Example*
  What current can a 230 V supply produce in a 1 kilohm resistor?

  Step 1 Put the information into symbol form and change to basic units.

  $V = 230$ V
  $R = 1 \text{ k}\Omega = 1000 \ \Omega$

  Step 2 Choose the correct equation.

  $$V = I R \implies I = \frac{V}{I}$$

  Step 3 Put the numbers into the equation and calculate the answer.

  $$I = \frac{V}{I} = \frac{230}{1000} = 0.23 \text{ A}$$

DO NOT FORGET UNITS.

❑ To find the total resistance R_T of resistors R_1 and R_2 connected in series the following equation is used:

$$R_T = R_1 + R_2$$

❑ To find the total resistance R_T of resistors R_1 and R_2 connected in parallel the following equation is used:

$$\frac{1}{R_T} = \frac{1}{R_1} + \frac{1}{R_2}$$

❑ If two identical resistors R are in parallel then R_T is $R/2$. If three identical resistors R are in parallel then R_T is $R/3$.

❑ *Example*
Find the total resistance of the following circuit.

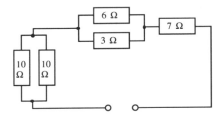

Step 1 Replace the pairs of resistors in parallel with the single equivalent resistor.

The two 10 Ω resistors in parallel, since identical, can be replaced by one 5 Ω resistor.

For the 6 Ω and the 3 Ω resistors in parallel:

$$\frac{1}{R_T} = \frac{1}{R_1} + \frac{1}{R_2} \quad => \quad \frac{1}{R_T} = \frac{1}{6} + \frac{1}{3}$$

Put both over a common denominator.

$$\frac{1}{R_T} = \frac{1+2}{6} = \frac{3}{6}$$

Turn both sides the other way up.

$$\frac{R_T}{1} = \frac{6}{3} = 2\,\Omega$$

Step 2 The circuit now becomes:

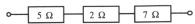

Apply resistors in series formula:

$$R_T = R_1 + R_2 + R_3$$
$$= 5 + 2 + 7 = 14\,\Omega$$

❏ Resistors can be used to split the supply voltage.

❏ A potential divider circuit consists of a number of resistors, or a variable resistor, connected across a supply.

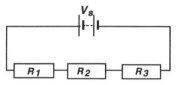

Total resistance $R_T = R_1 + R_2 + R_3$

$$V(R_1) = \frac{R_1}{R_1 + R_2 + R_3} \times V_s$$

where $V(R_1)$ is the voltage across R_1.

❏ *Example*

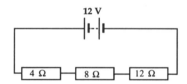

Total resistance = $4 + 8 + 12 = 24\,\Omega$

Voltage across $4\,\Omega$ = $\frac{4}{24} \times 12 = 2\,V$

Voltage across $8\,\Omega$ = $\frac{8}{24} \times 12 = 4\,V$

Voltage across $12\,\Omega$ = $\frac{12}{24} \times 12 = 6\,V$

2.2 ELECTRICAL ENERGY

❏ When there is an electric current in a component, there is an energy transformation, ie. electrical energy changes into another form of energy.

❏ Energy has the symbol **E**, and is measured in joules, J.

❏ Power has the symbol **P**, and is measured in watts, **W**. One watt is one joule per second: $1\,W = 1\,J\,s^{-1}$

❏ Energy is related to power and time by the equation:

$$E = Pt$$

where **E** is the energy in J
P is the power in W
t is the time in s

❏ *Example*
How long does it take for a 2.5 kW fire to use 30 MJ of energy?

Step 1 Put the information into symbol form and change to basic units.

$$P \quad = \quad 2.5\,kW \quad = \quad 2500\,W$$
$$E \quad = \quad 30\,MJ \quad = \quad 30\,000\,000\,J$$

Step 2 Choose the correct equation.

$$E = Pt \quad \Rightarrow \quad t = \frac{E}{P}$$

Step 3 Put the numbers into the equation and calculate the answer.

$$t = \frac{E}{P} = \frac{30\,000\,000}{2500} = 12\,000\,s = \textbf{200 mins}$$

DO NOT FORGET UNITS.

❏ The electrical energy transformed per second is given by **I V**.

❏ Electrical power is related to current and voltage by the equation:

$$P = IV$$

where **P** is the power in W
I is the current in A
V is the voltage in V

❑ *Example*

Find the current through a 2 kW heater connected to the mains supply.

Step 1 Put the information into symbol form and change to basic units.

$$P = 2\,kW = 2000\,W$$
$$V = 230\,V\,(\text{mains supply})$$

Step 2 Choose the correct equation.

$$P = IV \quad \Rightarrow \quad I = \frac{P}{V}$$

Step 3 Put the numbers into the equation and calculate the answer.

$$I = \frac{P}{V} = \frac{2000}{230} = 8.7\,A$$

DO NOT FORGET UNITS.

❑ Another expression for electrical power is:

$$\boxed{P = I^2 R}$$ where P is the power in W
I is the current in A
R is the resistance in Ω

❑ The two expressions

$$P = I^2 R \quad \text{and} \quad P = IV$$

can be shown to be equivalent:

$P = IV$ but from Ohm's law $V = IR$

Therefore $P = I\,(IR)$
$= I^2 R$

❑ The two expressions

$$P = \frac{V^2}{R} \quad \text{and} \quad P = IV$$

can be shown to be equivalent:

$P = IV$ but from Ohm's law $I = \dfrac{V}{R}$

Therefore $P = (\dfrac{V}{R})V = \dfrac{V^2}{R}$

❑ *Example*

What is the power dissipated in a 10 Ω
resistor with 50 mA through it?

Step 1 Put the information into symbol form and
change to basic units.

$$R = 10\,\Omega$$
$$I = 50\,\text{mA} = 0.05\,\text{A}$$

Step 2 Choose the correct equation.

$$P = I^2 R$$

Step 3 Put the numbers into the equation and
calculate the answer.

$$P = I^2 R = (0.05)^2 \times 10$$
$$= \textbf{0.025 W or 25 mW}$$

DO NOT FORGET UNITS.

❑ *Example*

What is the output voltage from a 50 W amplifier with
an output resistance of 15 Ω.

Step 1 Put the information into symbol form and
change to basic units.

$$P = 50\,\text{W}$$
$$R = 15\,\Omega$$

Step 2 Choose the correct equation.

$$P = \frac{V^2}{R} \quad \Rightarrow \quad V = \sqrt{PR}$$

Step 3 Put the numbers into the equation and
calculate the answer.

$$V = \sqrt{PR} = \sqrt{50 \times 15} = \sqrt{750}$$
$$= \textbf{27.4 V}$$

DO NOT FORGET UNITS.

❑ The two equations:

$$E = Pt \quad \text{and} \quad P = IV$$

can be combined to give:

$$\boxed{E = IVt}$$

where E is energy in J
I is current in A
V is voltage in V
t is time in s

❑ In a lamp, electrical energy is changed into heat and light.

❑ In an electric fire (heater) the energy change takes place in the resistance wire. This is called the element.

❑ Direct current (d.c.) is always in the same direction. Electrons flow from negative to positive.

❑ Alternating current (a.c.) changes direction many times every second.

❑ The mains supply is a.c. The frequency of the mains supply is 50 Hz.

❑ The mains voltage is 230 V.

❑ The quoted voltage of an a.c. supply, eg. 230 V for the mains, is the average (r.m.s.) value and is less than the peak value (325 V for the mains).

❑ A d.c. supply and an a.c. supply of the same quoted value will supply the same power to a given resistor.

2.3   ELECTROMAGNETISM

❑   When there is a current in a wire, there is a magnetic field round the wire.

❑   A voltage is induced in a conductor when:

  (1) the conductor is moving in a magnetic field,
  (2) the magnetic field is changing,
      eg. using a.c. to produce electromagnetism,
          switching on or off d.c. supply,
          moving the magnet.

❑   The induced voltage can be increased by:

  (1) increasing the magnetic field strength,
  (2) using more turns on the stator coil,
  (3) increasing the relative speed of the magnet (rotor) and the stator coil.

❑   The transformer consists of two coils of wire, with known number of turns, connected by a soft iron core:

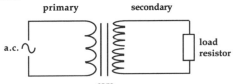

❑   The primary circuit is connected to the a.c. supply and the secondary supplies the resistor or 'load'. There is no electrical connection between the two circuits, only a magnetic one.

❑   Transformers work only on a.c.

❑   A transformer can change the magnitude (size) of an alternating voltage:

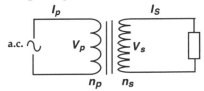

❑   The transformer equation states:

$$\boxed{\dfrac{V_p}{V_s} = \dfrac{n_p}{n_s}}$$

where V_p is the voltage across the primary coil
       V_s is the voltage across the secondary coil
       n_p is the number of turns in the primary coil
       n_s is the number of turns in secondary coil

❏ When $n_s > n_p$, then $V_s > V_p$.
   This is a step-up transformer.

❏ When $n_s < n_p$, then $V_s < V_p$.
   This is a step-down transformer.

❏ *Example*
   How many turns are needed on the secondary coil of a
   mains transformer with 5750 turns on the primary coil,
   if the output voltage is to be 12 V?

   Step 1 Put the information into symbol form.

   V_p = 230 V (mains supply)
   V_s = 12 V
   n_p = 5750

   Step 2 Choose the correct equation.

   NOTE : *The transformer equation can be turned upside*
   down and is still true. Write the equation so that
   the variable to be found is always on the top.

   $$\frac{V_p}{V_s} = \frac{n_p}{n_s}$$

   Step 3 Put the numbers into the equation and
   calculate the answer.

   $$\frac{V_p}{V_s} = \frac{n_p}{n_s} \quad => \quad \frac{12}{230} = \frac{n_s}{5750}$$

   $$n_s = \frac{12 \times 5750}{230} = \textbf{300 turns}$$

   DO NOT FORGET UNITS.

❏ If the transformer is assumed to be **100% efficient** then
   the power into the transformer is equal to the power
   given out:

   $$P_p = P_s$$

   $$I_p V_p = I_s V_s$$

   This can be written: $\boxed{\dfrac{V_p}{V_s} = \dfrac{I_s}{I_p}}$

❏ The full transformer equation is given by:

   $$\boxed{\dfrac{V_p}{V_s} = \dfrac{I_s}{I_p} = \dfrac{n_p}{n_s}}$$

2.3   ELECTRONIC COMPONENTS

❑   In **output devices** each case the main energy change is
     from electrical to some other form:

Device	Output energy
Motor	kinetic (rotation)
Solenoid	kinetic (in straight line)
Buzzer	sound
Loudspeaker	sound
LED	light
Relay	kinetic
7- segment display	light

❑   The symbol for an **LED** (light emitting diode) is:

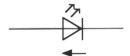

direction of electron flow

❑   An LED will only allow current through it in one
     direction. Therefore it only lights when connected the
     correct way round.

❑   An LED will be damaged if too large a current passes
     through it. A series resistor limits the size of the current
     so that the LED is not damaged.

❑   The following circuit will allow the LED to light:

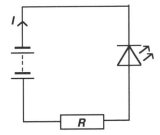

     The value of the series resistor required for a given LED
     and given supply can be calculated.

❑ **Example**
If the LED takes 10 mA and 2 V to work correctly,
calculate the series resistor required with a 5 V supply.

Step 1 As the supply voltage is 5 V and the LED
requires 2 V, the voltage across the series
resistor is:

5 - 2 = 3 V

NOTE : *Voltages in series add up to the supply voltage.*

Step 2 Change the current through the series
resistor to basic units.

I = 10 mA = 0.01 A

NOTE : *The current is the same at all points in a series
circuit.*

Step 3 Calculate the resistance using Ohm's law.

$$V = IR \implies R = \frac{V}{I} = \frac{3}{0.01} = 300 \ \Omega$$

DO NOT FORGET UNITS.

Input devices

❑ A microphone changes sound energy into electrical
energy.
Symbol

❑ A thermocouple changes heat into electrical energy.
Symbol

❑ A solar cell changes light energy into electrical energy.
Symbol

❑ A thermistor is a resistor, the resistance of which varies
with temperature. For most common thermistors, as
the temperature increases the resistance decreases.
Symbol

❑ An LDR is a light dependent resistor. As the light
intensity increases, the resistance decreases.
Symbol

❑   Ohm's law, $V = IR$, can be used to calculate the resistance of either a thermistor or an LDR.

❑   A transistor can be used as a switch.

❑   A transistor can be either ON or OFF, ie. it either conducts and allows a current through it or it does not.

> **NOTE :** *You need to know about two types of transistor - MOSFET and npn.*

❑   The symbol for an n-channel enhancement MOSFET is:

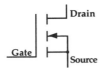

MOSFET stands for **metal-oxide-semiconductor-field-effect-transistor**

❑   The symbol for an **npn** transistor is:

where   **b** is the base
        e is the emitter
        c is the collector

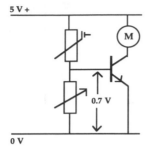

The circuit switches the motor on when it gets hot.

☐ For the transistor to switch on, there must be 0.7 V across the base - emitter junction. As the thermistor heats up its resistance decreases so the voltage across it decreases. The voltage across the variable resistor increases to more than 0.7 V and the transistor switches on.

☐

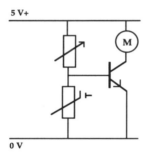

The circuit switches the motor off when it gets hot or it switches the motor on when it gets cold.

☐ As the thermistor heats up, its resistance decreases so the voltage across it falls below 0.7 V and the transistor switches off.

❑

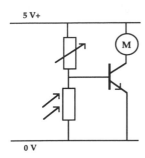

The circuit switches the motor on when it gets dark.

❑ As light intensity falls, the resistance of the LDR increases. The voltage across the LDR increases to more than 0.7 V, the transistor switches the motor on.

❑

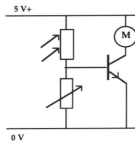

The circuit switches on the motor when it gets light.

❑ As light intensity increases the LDR has lower resistance and less voltage across it. Therefore the voltage across the variable resistor increases to more than 0.7 V and the transistor switches the motor on.

❑ In each of the previous circuits the variable resistor is present to allow the exact point at which the transistor switches to be adjusted.

❑ In each of the previous circuits the **npn** transistor can be replaced with a **MOSFET** transistor. The gate voltage, to switch on the transistor, would be about 2 V.

❑ An **amplifier** increases the strength of an electrical signal.

❑ The **output signal** from an amplifier has the **same frequency** but a **larger amplitude** than the input signal.

❑ Amplifiers are used in:

(1) radios,
(2) televisions,
(3) HiFi systems,
(4) baby alarms,
(5) many other systems where the detector (of heat, light, pressure, etc.) produces a small voltage.

❑ The **voltage gain** of an amplifier is given by:

$$\text{voltage gain} = \frac{\text{output voltage}}{\text{input voltage}}$$

❑ *Example*
What will be the output voltage of an amplifier with a gain of 90, when the input voltage is 5 mV?

Step 1 Put the information into symbol form and change to basic units.

Gain = 90
Input voltage = 5 mV = 0.005 V

Step 2 Choose the correct equation.

$$\text{voltage gain} = \frac{\text{output voltage}}{\text{input voltage}} \quad =>$$

output voltage = voltage gain x input voltage

Step 3 Put the numbers into the equation and calculate the answer.

output voltage = voltage gain x input voltage
= 90 x 0.005 = **0.45 V**

❑ An oscilloscope can be used to find the voltage gain of an amplifier:

(1) Measure the input voltage to the amplifier.
(2) Measure the output voltage of the amplifier.
(3) Use the voltage gain equation to calculate gain.

UNIT 3   WAVES AND OPTICS

3.1   WAVES

❑   A wave transfers energy.

❑   **Measuring the speed of sound in air**

One method uses large cymbals a long distance from the observer. The cymbals are clashed together to produce a sound. The large distance between the observer and the cymbals is measured. The stopwatch is started when the cymbals are seen to move together and stopped when the sound is heard. The speed of sound is then calculated from the equation:

$$v = \frac{d}{t}$$

For accuracy, the process is repeated and the average taken.

❑   Radio and television signals are transmitted through air at 300 million m s^{-1}.
The speed of light in air is also 3×10^8 m s^{-1}.

❑   The speed of sound in air is about 330 m s^{-1}.

❑   *Example*
How far will a radio signal travel in 1 minute?

Step 1   Put the information into symbol form and change to basic units.

v $= 3 \times 10^8$ m s^{-1}
t $= 1$ minute $= 60$ s

NOTE : *If the problem involves light, radio or television you are expected to know that the speed is 3×10^8 m s^{-1}.*

Step 2   Choose the correct equation.

$d = v\,t$

Step 3   Put the numbers into the equation and calculate the answer.

$d = v\,t$ $= 3 \times 10^8 \times 60 = \mathbf{1.8 \times 10^{10}}$ **m**

DO NOT FORGET UNITS.

- ❑ The **wavelength**, λ, of a wave is the minimum distance in which the wave repeats. It is measured in metres, **m**.

- ❑ The **frequency**, **f**, of a wave is the number of waves per second and is measured in hertz, **Hz**.

- ❑ The **period**, **T**, of a wave is the time taken for one wave to pass a point or for one wave to be transmitted. It is measured in seconds, **s**.

- ❑ The **wave speed**, **v**, is the distance travelled in one second and is measured in metres per second, **m s^{-1}**.

- ❑ The **amplitude**, **a**, of a wave is the distance from the centre to the top of a crest or the bottom of a trough.

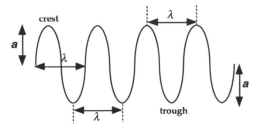

- ❑ Wave speed, frequency and wavelength are related by the wave equation:

$$v = f \lambda$$

- ❑ The frequency of a wave is the same as the frequency of the source which produces the wave.

- ❑ The time period in seconds is given by 1/frequency:

$$T = \frac{1}{f} \quad \text{or} \quad f = \frac{1}{T}$$

- ❑ In a transverse wave, the vibrations are at right angles to the direction of travel of the energy.

- ❑ Waves on strings, water waves, light waves and all members of the electromagnetic spectrum are transverse waves.

- ❑ In a longitudinal wave the vibrations are in the same direction as the energy travels.

- ❑ Sound is a longitudinal wave.

❑ *Example*
A wave travels 50 cm in 5 s.
If its frequency is 2 Hz, find
(a) its speed,
(b) its wavelength.

Step 1   Put the information into symbol form and
          change to basic units.

          d = 50 cm = 0.5 m
          t = 5 s
          f = 2 Hz

Step 2   Choose the correct equation for part **(a)**.

          $$d = vt \Rightarrow v = \frac{d}{t}$$

Step 3   Put the numbers into the equation and
          calculate the answer.

          $$v = \frac{d}{t} = \frac{0.5}{5} = 0.1 \text{ m s}^{-1}$$

Repeat steps 2 and 3 for part **(b)**.

          $$v = f\lambda \Rightarrow \lambda = \frac{v}{f} = \frac{0.1}{2} = 0.05 \text{ m}$$

DO NOT FORGET UNITS.

❑   There are a number of waves which travel at the speed
    of light. They differ in their wavelength and frequency.

❑   These waves are members of the **electromagnetic
    spectrum**

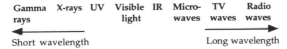

| Gamma rays | X-rays | UV | Visible light | IR | Micro- waves | TV waves | Radio waves |

Short wavelength   Long wavelength

where **UV** is ultraviolet and **IR** is infrared (also known
as heat radiation).

3.2   REFLECTION

❑   Light can be reflected.

❑   Light travels in straight lines and ray paths are
     reversible.

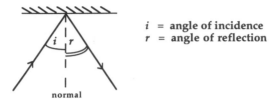

i = **angle of incidence**
r = **angle of reflection**

normal

The law of reflection states that the angle of incidence is
equal to the angle of reflection.

❑   A **transmitter** uses a curved reflector to transmit the
     signal as a **parallel beam**.

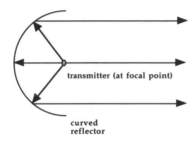

transmitter (at focal point)

curved
reflector

❑   The signal can be light, sound, microwaves or infrared
     using an appropriate transmitter. In each case the
     curved reflector can produce a parallel beam.

❑   A receiver uses a curved reflector to collect the signal
     over a large area and bring it to a **focus**.
     The aerial is placed at the focus.

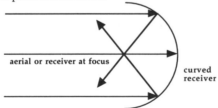

aerial or receiver at focus

curved
receiver

❑   The signal can be light, sound, microwaves or infrared.
     In each case the curved reflector can focus the signal
     onto an appropriate detector.

- Satellites allow direct communication throughout the world.

- The period of a **satellite** (time taken for it to orbit the Earth) depends on the height above the Earth.

- A **geostationary satellite** orbits in 24 hours and therefore stays above the same point on the Earth's surface.

- Three geostationary satellites on the equator allow world-wide communication, with each satellite linking with ground stations on different continents.

- A **ground station** uses a curved reflector to transmit the microwave signal as a **parallel beam** to the satellite.

- The satellite has a curved receiver to collect the signal over a large area and bring it to a **focus**.
  The aerial is placed at the focus.

- At the satellite the signal is amplified and has the frequency changed. The signal is then sent back to Earth. This time the curved transmitter on the satellite sends out a parallel beam and the curved satellite dishes on houses, etc. collect the signal over the large area of the dish and focus it to make the signal stronger.

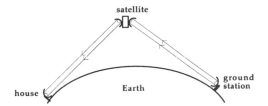

3.3   REFRACTION

❏   Refraction of light is a change of speed which occurs
    when light moves from one material into another and is
    usually accompanied by a change in direction:

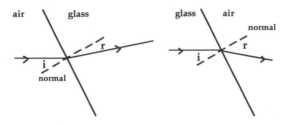

❏   *i* is the angle of incidence.
    r is the angle of refraction.
    The **normal** is a construction line at right angles to the
    boundary at the point where the incident ray meets the
    boundary.

.❏   When light travels from glass to air, it bends away from
    the normal. As the angle of incidence is increased the
    last ray of light which can escape meets the boundary at
    the **critical angle (C)** and emerges at 90° to the normal:

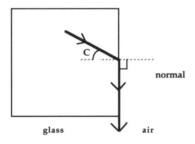

❏   Any ray incident on the boundary at an angle greater
    than the critical angle will undergo **total internal
    reflection (TIR)**.

❏   Light travels along optical fibres by total internal
    reflection:

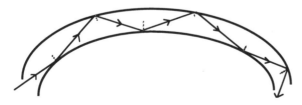

❑ The signal is made up of variations in the light and these are transmitted very quickly to the other end of the optical fibre.

❑ Given either the distance travelled in the glass or the time taken, the other can be calculated using the equation $d = v\,t$ and the speed of light, which is 2×10^8 m s^{-1} in the glass.

❑ There are two main shapes of lens:

Convex (converging)   **Concave** (diverging)

❑ A converging (convex) lens brings parallel light to a focus.

❑ A diverging (concave) lens causes parallel light to diverge as though it came from an imaginary focus on the same side of the lens as the incident light.

❑ The **focal length** of a convex lens is the distance between the lens and the point where parallel rays are brought to a focus. This can be measured experimentally by obtaining a clear image of a distant object, eg. the view from a window, onto a screen. The focal length is the distance between the lens and the screen.

❑ A ray diagram allows the position and size of the image to be found.

❑ For a convex lens, the position of any image can be found by drawing two rays from the top of the object:

    (1) a ray through the centre of the lens which does not change direction

    (2) a ray parallel to the principal axis which goes through the focus

❑ A real image is produced when the two rays cross. A screen placed at that point would have a clear picture produced on it.

❑ The image produced depends on the position of the object in front of the lens, compared with the focal length of the lens.

❑ If the object is more than two focal lengths from the lens. The image is real, inverted (upside down) and smaller than the object (diminished).

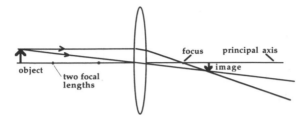

❑ If the object is between one and two focal lengths from the lens the image is real, inverted (upside down) and larger than the object (magnified).

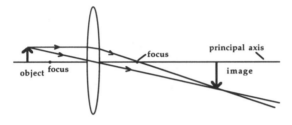

❑ If the object is less than one focal lengths from the lens. The image is virtual, erect (right way up) and larger than the object (magnified).

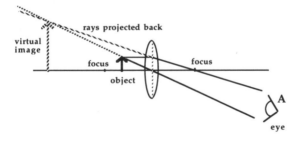

❑ In this case the construction rays do not meet, but when projected back they do meet. Since light does not actually pass through this point the image is **virtual**. The image cannot be produced on a screen. However a human eye placed at **A** will bring the light to a focus and the virtual magnified image is seen.

❑ A magnifying glass is a convex lens with the object placed between the lens and the focus.

❑ The lens in the eye can change shape. This is called **accommodation**.

❑ Light rays coming from a **distant object** arrive at the eye parallel. The lens is **thin**:

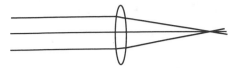

❑ Light rays from a **nearby object** diverge. The lens is much **thicker**:

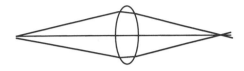

❑ People can only see clearly if the light is focused on the retina.

❑ In **long sight**, light from nearby objects is focused behind the retina and only objects a long way away are clear.

❑ In **short sight**, light from distant objects is focused in front of the retina and only objects close at hand are clear.

❑ Both long and short sight can be corrected using lenses.

❑ **Long sight**

Use of a convex lens causes light to converge more so that it is focused on the retina:

❑ **Short sight**

Use of a concave lens causes light to diverge before it enters the eye so that the eye focuses it on the retina:

❑ The **power** of a lens is measured in **dioptres, D.**

❑ Power is related to focal length by the equation:

> or
>
> $$\text{power of lens} = \frac{1}{\text{focal length (in metres)}}$$
>
> $$\text{focal length} = \frac{1}{\text{power}}$$

❑ Both focal length and power are:

> **negative** for **concave lens**
> **positive** for **convex lens**

❑ *Example*
A lens has a focal length of -25 cm. Find the power of the lens and state whether it is concave or convex.

Step 1   Put the information into symbol form and change to basic units.

$$f = -25 \text{ cm} = -0.25 \text{ m}$$

Step 2   Choose the correct equation.

$$\text{power} = \frac{1}{f}$$

Step 3   Put the numbers into the equation and calculate the answer.

$$\text{power} = \frac{1}{f} = \frac{-1}{0.25} = -4 \text{ D}$$

Since the power is negative, it is a concave lens.

DO NOT FORGET UNITS.

NOTE : *Focal lengths are nearly always given in centimetres and **must** be changed to metres.*

4.1   IONISING RADIATIONS

❏ The **atom** consists of a central **nucleus** with orbiting **electrons**.

❏ The nucleus contains positively charged **protons** and uncharged **neutrons**. It has nearly all of the mass of the atom and all the positive charge.

❏ The **electrons** are negatively charged and much lighter than neutrons or protons (1/2000 the mass).

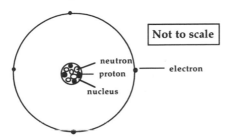

❏ An atom is electrically neutral as it has the same number of negative electrons orbiting the nucleus as positive protons in the nucleus.

❏ The energy carried by radiation can be absorbed by the material it is passing through.

❏ There are three types of radiation:

     alpha   -   α
     beta   -   β
     gamma   -   γ

❏ These three radiations can be identified by their different absorption properties.

❏ The source is placed in front of a Geiger-Muller tube and the amount of radiation passing through the absorber registers on the scaler. Various absorbers can be used:

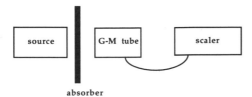

❑ Alpha radiation is absorbed by paper.
Beta radiation is absorbed by a few millimetres of aluminium.
Gamma radiation is absorbed by a few centimetres of lead.

❑ Alpha radiation is absorbed by a few centimetres of air.
Beta radiation is absorbed by a few metres of air.
Gamma radiation is not absorbed by air.

❑ An **alpha particle** is a helium nucleus. It has two protons and two neutrons.

❑ A **beta particle** is a high energy electron from the nucleus. It is created when a neutron decays into an electron and a proton.

❑ **Gamma radiation** is very high frequency, short wavelength electromagnetic radiation.

❑ **Ionisation** occurs when the atom gains an electron to give it an overall negative charge, or loses an electron to give it an overall positive charge.

❑ When radiation passes through a material it can ionise the atoms of that material.

❑ Alpha particles produce much greater ionisation density than beta particles or gamma rays.

❑ Radiation will fog photographic plates.

❑ This is used in film badges. Various parts of the film are covered by different thicknesses of various absorbers. When the badge is developed, the film will only be affected if radiation has passed through the absorber. By examining which areas are affected, the type and amount of radiation can be determined.

❑ Radiation is absorbed by some materials and the energy re-emitted as light, called scintillations.

❑ This effect is used in scintillation counters and gamma cameras.

❏ The Geiger-Muller tube is a detector of radiation.

❏ Ionisation takes place in the Geiger-Muller tube:

cylindrical outer electrode

low pressure gas

mica window

central electrode

cable to scaler

❏ A current cannot normally pass between the central electrode and the cylindrical outer electrode but when the gas becomes ionised it allows a current to pass. This pulse of current is measured on the scaler. The window is very thin mica to allow even alpha particles into the tube.

❏ Radiation can kill or change the nature of living cells.

❏ Radiation can be used to:
(1) sterilise instruments by killing germs,
(2) kill the cells which make up a cancerous tumour.

❏ Radioactive material can be detected by the radiation it gives off. Usually gamma rays are used since these can be detected outside the body.

❏ A **tracer** is a radioactive substance which is either injected into the body or swallowed. The tracer is concentrated in the organ the doctor wishes to examine and the movement of the tracer is measured by the gamma radiation, eg. tracers can be used to study the uptake of iodine by the thyroid gland.

❏ Tracers are also used in industry and agriculture, eg. to find cracks in pipes. The radioactive substance is added to the fluid in the pipe and the detector can then find where it leaks out of the pipe.

4.2   DOSIMETRY

❑   **The activity, *A*,** of a radioactive source is measured in **becquerels, Bq,** where 1 Bq is one atom decaying per second.

❑   The effects of absorbed radiation depends not only on the amount of the radiation but also on the size of the object which absorbs it.

❑   The **absorbed dose, *D*,** is the energy, ***E*,** absorbed per unit mass, ***m*,** of the absorbing material.

❑   The absorbed dose is measured in **grays, Gy,** where $1 \text{ Gy} = 1 \text{ J kg}^{-1}$.

❑   The risk of biological harm from an exposure to radiation depends on:

   (1) the absorbed dose,
   (2) the kind of radiation, eg. α, β, γ, or slow neutrons,
   (3) the body organs or tissues exposed.

❑   Each type of radiation is allocated a **quality factor, *Q*.** This is just a number which compares the biological effect of the radiation.

❑   The **dose equivalent, *H*,** which is measured in **sieverts, Sv,** takes into account the type and energy of the radiation. The same dose equivalent in **Sv** always gives the same biological effect.

❑   The dose equivalent is given by the absorbed dose multiplied by the quality factor:

$$H = D\,Q$$

   where ***D*** is in Gy
   Q is the quality factor
   H is in Sv

❑   Since the quality factor is a non-dimensional number, the units of ***H*** are the same as those of ***D*.** Therefore one sievert is also equal to one joule per kilogram, $(1 \text{ Sv} = 1 \text{ J kg}^{-1})$.

❑   When calculating the overall effect of radiation from various sources, the dose equivalent of each source must be calculated before adding up to the final total.

❏ *Example*
A worker is exposed to 15 mGy of γ - radiation,
400 μGy of fast neutrons and 600 μGy of α - particles in
the course of a year. What is his total dose equivalent?

The quality factors are: $\quad\gamma$ - radiation $\quad$ - $\quad$ 1
$\qquad\qquad\qquad\qquad$ fast neutrons $\quad$ - $\quad$ 10
$\qquad\qquad\qquad\qquad$ α - particles $\quad$ - $\quad$ 20

Step 1 Put the information into symbol form.
$$D_\gamma = 15\,\text{mGy} = 15 \times 10^{-3}\,\text{Gy}$$
$$Q_\gamma = 1$$
$$D_n = 400\,\mu\text{Gy} = 400 \times 10^{-6}\,\text{Gy}$$
$$Q_n = 10$$
$$D_\alpha = 600\,\mu\text{Gy} = 600 \times 10^{-6}\,\text{Gy}$$
$$Q_\alpha = 20$$

Step 2 Choose the correct equation.

$$H = D\ Q$$

Step 3 Put the numbers into the equation and
$\qquad\qquad$ calculate the answer.

γ - radiation $\quad = \quad 15 \times 10^{-3} \quad \times 1 \quad = \quad 15 \times 10^{-3}$ Sv
fast neutrons $\quad = \quad 400 \times 10^{-6} \quad \times 10 \ = \quad 4 \times 10^{-6}$ Sv
α - radiation $\quad = \quad 600 \times 10^{-6} \quad \times 20 \ = \quad 12 \times 10^{-6}$ Sv

$\qquad\qquad$ Total dose equivalent $\qquad = \quad \textbf{31} \times \textbf{10}^{-3}$ **Sv**
$\qquad\qquad\qquad\qquad\qquad\qquad\qquad\qquad$ **(31 mSv)**

DO NOT FORGET UNITS.

❏ Different tissues in the body vary in their susceptibility
to damage from radiation.

❏ The **effective dose equivalent** is measured in sieverts
and takes account of the type of tissue. It is used to
indicate the risk to health from exposure to ionising
radiation.

❏ We are exposed to continual background radiation.

❏ Typical annual dose equivalent values for various
sources of background radiation are:

Cosmic radiation	0.3 mSv
Radioactivity from rocks, soil, buildings	0.3 mSv
Radioactivity present in the human body	0.4 mSv
Inhaled radon and daughter products	1.0 mSv
Total exposure	**2.0 mSv**

❑ Cosmic rays are radiations from outer space, consisting of many different type of particles and electromagnetic radiation. The atmosphere absorbs much of the radiation and the dose equivalent varies with altitude. High flying planes can be exposed to much higher levels of radiation from cosmic rays and may sometimes move to a lower level if the cosmic radiation is at a particularly high level.

❑ Rocks, soils and building materials, especially granite, often contain radioactive material. Aberdeen, 'The Granite City' has a dose equivalent of about 1.7 mSv annually, while Kerala in India has thorium in the soil and has an annual dose equivalent of about 20 mSv.

❑ Human bodies contain some radioactive isotopes such as potassium and carbon. These come from the air we breathe and the food we eat.

❑ The main source of exposure comes from radon and its daughter products. Radon can accumulate in buildings from the material of which they are made.

❑ Artificial sources of radiation such as medical X - rays, nuclear reactors, etc. can add about another 0.28 mSv per year.

4.3   HALF-LIFE AND SAFETY

❏   The activity of a radioactive source decreases with time.

❏   The decay of an individual atom is a totally random event and cannot be predicted.

❏   However, the time taken for half the atoms in a sample of a particular material to decay is always the same. This is called the **half-life.**

❏   The half-life is the time taken for the activity of a sample to drop by half.

❏   The half-life can be found from an Activity/Time graph. This is obtained by placing the source in front of a Geiger-Muller tube, measuring the activity every minute and plotting the results:

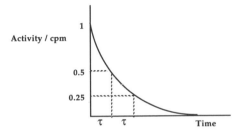

On the graph mark the initial activity, then draw a line parallel to the time axis at half this activity (any initial activity can be chosen).
From the point where the line meets the curve, draw a line parallel to the activity axis.
The half-life is given by the point where the line cuts the time axis.

❏   The half-life will always be the same for a given radioactive material.

NOTE : *There are two main type of problems involving half-life:*

❑ *Example 1*
If a source of activity 4000 kBq has a half-life of 3 days, what is its activity 18 days later?

$$\text{Number of half-lives} = \frac{\text{number of days}}{\text{half-life in days}} = \frac{18}{3} = 6$$

$$4000 \xrightarrow{1\tau} 2000 \xrightarrow{2\tau} 1000 \xrightarrow{3\tau} 500 \xrightarrow{4\tau} 250 \xrightarrow{5\tau} 125 \xrightarrow{6\tau} 62.5$$

The activity after 18 days is **62.5 kBq.**

❑ *Example 2*
If a source of activity 1600 kBq has dropped to an activity of 200 kBq in 30 days, what is the half-life of the source?

$$1600 \xrightarrow{1\tau} 800 \xrightarrow{2\tau} 400 \xrightarrow{3\tau} 200$$

The number of half-lives is 3.

$$\text{half-life in days} = \frac{\text{number of days}}{\text{number of half-lives}}$$

$$= \frac{30}{3}$$

$$= 10$$

The half-life is **10 days.**

❑ Safety precautions for handling radioactive material include:

(1) Always use forceps to handle sources.
(2) Make sure the source is never pointed at anyone.
(3) Store in lead-lined boxes.
(4) Label all radioactive material.

❑ The exposure (dose-equivalent) from any particular source can be reduced by shielding, ie. by placing some absorbing material between the source and the people.

❑ Suitable absorbing materials are lead and thick concrete.

❑ The exposure (dose-equivalent) from any particular source can be reduced by limiting the time of exposure.

❑ The exposure (dose-equivalent) from any particular source can be reduced by increasing the distance from the source.

❏ The radioactive hazard sign is yellow and black.

❏ This hazard symbol must be displayed when radioactive material is used and also where the material is stored.

❏ In **fission**, a large nucleus splits into two nuclei of smaller mass with the release of several neutrons and energy:

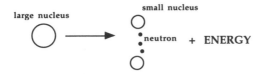

❏ **Spontaneous fission** occurs when the large nucleus splits without outside influence. This process has a half-life.

❏ **Induced fission** occurs when a neutron hits the nucleus. There is no half-life for this process.

❏ In a **chain reaction**, a neutron hits a nucleus of uranium causing it to split up. This gives two different smaller nuclei and two or three unattached neutrons, which move on to hit other uranium nuclei and repeat the reaction:

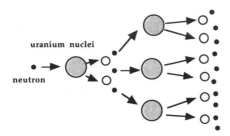

❏ In a power station, stored energy is turned into electrical energy. The stored energy can be:

(1) chemical energy in fossil fuels (coal, gas, oil)
(2) nuclear energy (usually from uranium)

❏ Thermal power stations burn fossil fuels to provide heat, which is then changed to electricity.

❏ Nuclear reactors use the energy from fissions to provide heat, which is then changed to electricity.

❏ Advantages of nuclear power are:

  (1) For the same amount of electricity a much smaller mass of uranium is required compared to fossil fuels.
  (2) Nuclear power stations do not contribute to the greenhouse effect; thermal power stations do.
  (3) Small amounts of waste is produced for large amounts of nuclear energy produced.
  (4) Fast breeder reactors can produce more fuel, plutonium, for use in other reactors.

❏ Disadvantages of nuclear power are:

  (1) The risk of a nuclear accident, which could harm a large number of people.
  (2) Nuclear waste remains dangerous for a very long time.
  (3) Plutonium is produced which could be used in nuclear bombs.
  (4) Uranium is a non-renewable source of energy.

❏ Nuclear waste can be divided into three categories:

  (1) Low level radioactive waste, both solid and liquid.
  (2) Medium level solid radioactive waste.
  (3) High level radioactive waste.

❏ The first two categories do not cause major problems. Many industries produce waste products and the low and medium level waste from nuclear reactors can be treated in the same way. It is regulated by the government because it is radioactive.

❏ The high level waste is a major problem as it will remain dangerous for more than 100 000 years.

❏ The high level waste has to be carefully stored in deep vaults in stable geological formations. Noone wants the waste stored near them.

❏ There is research into safer methods of storing the waste.

❏ The core of the nuclear reactor consists of:
fuel elements
moderator
control rods
coolant
containment vessel

❏ The **fuel element** consists of 36 fuel rods each containing enriched uranium pellets.

❏ Enriched uranium contains a higher percentage of the uranium-235 isotope, which undergoes fission, than normal uranium.

❏ The neutrons given off from a fission have to be slowed down if they are to cause further fissions. This is done by collisions with the molecules of the **moderator**.

❏ The moderator is usually graphite or heavy water.

❏ If all the neutrons produced by fission go onto cause further fissions, the chain reaction is uncontrolled. This produces a bomb.

❏ In a nuclear reactor only one neutron per fission is allowed, on average, to cause a further fission. This is a controlled chain reaction.

❏ Unwanted neutrons are absorbed by the **control rods**.

❏ The control rods are usually made of boron.

❏ These rods are placed between the fuel rods and lowered or raised to maintain the required level of fission within the reactor.

❏ Spare control rods are kept above the reactor core to be lowered in the event of an emergency and stop the chain reaction.

❏ Heat produced from the reaction has to be transferred from the core to produce steam. The steam is then used to drive turbines and produce electricity.

❏ The transfer of heat is carried out by the **coolant** often high pressure carbon dioxide gas.

❏ The core is surrounded by the **containment vessel**. This is usually thick reinforced concrete lined with steel.

❏ The containment vessel must be thick enough to reduce radiation (gamma rays and neutrons) to a safe level.

❏ The containment vessel must also protect the core from outside problems, eg. plane crashes, earthquakes. It must contain all the contents of the core in the event of an emergency.

QUANTITIES AND UNITS

Quantity	Symbol	Unit (SI unit first)
length	l	m, mm, cm, km
area	A	m^2, cm^2, mm^2
volume	V	m^3, cm^3, m
distance	d	m, cm, km
displacement	s	m, cm, km
mass	m	kg, g
weight	W	N
time	t	s, m, hr
half life	τ	s, m, hr, yr
velocity	v	m s^{-1}
acceleration	a	m s^{-2}
gravitational field strength	g	N kg^{-1}
frequency	f	Hz (hertz), kHz
wavelength	λ	m, cm
period	T	s
energy	E	J (joule)
work	E_w	J
force	F	N (newton)
power	P	W (watt)
momentum	p	kg m s^{-1}
power of lens	P	D (dioptre)
current	I	A (ampere)
voltage (p.d.)	V	V (volt)
resistance	R	Ω (ohm)
charge	Q	C (coulomb) , μC
temperature	T	^{o}C
specific heat capacity	c	J kg^{-1} ^{o}C^{-1}
specific latent heat	L	J kg^{-1}
activity	A	Bq (bequerel)
absorbed dose	D	Gy (gray)
dose equivalent	H	Sv (sievert)

Other symbols

acc. due to gravity	g	9.8 m s^{-2}
quality factor	Q	-

UNIT 1

KINEMATICS

❑   Average speed = $\dfrac{\text{total distance}}{\text{total time}}$

❑   Average velocity = $\dfrac{\text{displacement}}{\text{total time}}$

❑ $\bar{v} = \dfrac{d}{t}$ (only for constant or average speed)

❑   Distance = area under speed - time graph

❑   A vector quantity has magnitude (size) and direction, eg. displacement, velocity, acceleration, force, weight, momentum.

❑   A scalar quantity has magnitude only, eg. distance, speed, energy, power, time.

❑   Vectors must be added 'nose to tail' either by a scale diagram or, if vectors are at right angles, by Pythagoras'. When the result is quoted it **must** include a direction.

❑   Note that the term $\dfrac{(u + v)}{2} = \bar{v}$ where $\bar{v}$ = average speed.

❑   **Light gate**
instantaneous velocity = $v = \dfrac{\text{length of card}}{\text{time to cut beam}}$

DYNAMICS

❑   The newton is the net force required to give a mass of 1 kg an acceleration of 1 m s^{-2}.

❑   **Newton's First Law**
A body remains at rest or continues at a constant velocity unless acted upon by an unbalanced force.

❑   **Newton's Second Law**
$F = m\,a$ where F is the unbalanced force in the direction of the motion.

❑ $W = m\,g$

❑ $a = \dfrac{v - u}{t}$

❑ $v = u + a\,t$

❑   **Newton's Third Law**
If **A** exerts a force on **B**, **B** exerts an equal force on **A** in the opposite direction.

MOMENTUM AND ENERGY

❏ $E_w = F d$

❏ $E_p = m g h$

❏ $E_k = \frac{1}{2} m v^2$

❏ $v = \sqrt{2 g h}$ since $E_k = E_p$
(Do not use if energy is 'lost' due to friction.)

❏ **Energy conservation**
If there is apparent energy loss it is usually due to work done against friction:
$F d$ = **lost energy**   where F is the frictional force
                                  d is the displacement

❏ $P = \dfrac{E}{t}$ ($P = F v$ for **constant speed**)

❏ **momentum** $= m v$

❏ Momentum is conserved in explosions and collisions, provided no external forces act.

❏ In explosions the initial momentum is zero. Therefore the total momentum after the explosion is zero.

HEAT

❏ $E_h = c m \Delta T$

❏ $E_h = m L$

❏ L vaporisation - if boiling or condensing

❏ L fusion - if melting or freezing

❏ efficiency $= \dfrac{E_{out}}{E_{in}} \times 100\%$ or $\dfrac{P_{out}}{P_{in}} \times 100\%$

UNIT 2

CIRCUITS

- $Q = I t$

- $V = I R$

- $P = I V = I^2 R = \dfrac{V^2}{R}$

- $E = I t V = I^2 R t = \dfrac{V^2 t}{R}$

- $R_T = R_1 + R_2 + R_3 + \ldots$ resistors in series

- $\dfrac{1}{R_T} = \dfrac{1}{R_1} + \dfrac{1}{R_2} + \dfrac{1}{R_3} + \ldots$ resistors in parallel

- $\dfrac{V_s}{V_p} = \dfrac{n_s}{n_p} = \dfrac{I_p}{I_s}$ Transformer equation for 100 % efficiency: **s** indicates secondary, **p** indicates primary circuit

- $V_{(R_1)} = \dfrac{R_1}{R_1 + R_2 + R_3}$

- voltage gain $= \dfrac{\text{voltage out}}{\text{voltage in}}$

- power gain $= \dfrac{\text{power out}}{\text{power in}}$

UNIT 3

WAVES AND LIGHT

- $v = f \lambda$

- $f = \dfrac{1}{T}$ or $T = \dfrac{1}{f}$

-
| Gamma rays | X-rays | UV | Visible light | IR | Micro-waves | TV waves | Radio waves |

← Short wavelength   Long wavelength →

- power of lens $= \dfrac{1}{\text{focal length (in metres)}}$

- focal length $= \dfrac{1}{\text{power}}$

UNIT 4

RADIOACTIVITY

❑ $\quad A = \dfrac{N}{t}\qquad$ where N is the number of atomic nuclei decaying

❑ $\quad D = \dfrac{E}{m}$

❑ $\quad H = D\,Q$

DRAWING AND INTERPRETING GRAPHS

Drawing graphs

❑ 1. If you have to choose the scale of the axes:
   (a) find maximum value needed for each axis,
   (b) make the scales simple to interpret, (avoid using 1 box to represent 3 units),
   (c) **x-axis:** the numbers usually rise in regular intervals (the independent variable),
   (d) **y-axis:** the experimental results, usually irregular.

❑ 2. Label the axes clearly with both the name of the variable and the units.

❑ 3. When marking the points use a +.
   Double check any points that are well away from the others.

❑ 4. Join the points with a smooth line.
   If the graph is obviously a straight line then use a ruler to draw the best fitting line that you can.

Interpreting graphs

❑ 1. (a) Check very carefully the information given in the question.
   (b) Check the variables plotted on the axes.
   (c) Check the units of the variables.

❑ 2. Read values carefully.

❑ 3. To find value of x given that of y:
   (a) draw a line across from the given value of y, parallel to the x-axis, until it meets the curve,
   (b) draw a line down from that point to the x-axis, parallel to the y-axis and read the value on the x-axis.

USING EQUATIONS

There are no short cuts!

☐ 1. **Learn the formulae.**
You must know all of them, **accurately.**

☐ 2. Read the question carefully and even if you do not know how to do it, follow the steps below. If you know your formulae you may see the way to handle the question once you have started.

☐ 3. Write out the values given in the question using symbol, value and units, including the symbol for the required answer:

symbol = value and units

eg. v = 200 cm s^{-1}

☐ 4. Change any non-standard units to the basic unit (shown first in the list of units),

eg. v = 0.2 m s^{-1}

☐ 5. Write down the equation which involves the symbols that you have, in its usual form,

eg. $E_h = c\,m\,\Delta T$

☐ 6. Rearrange the equation so that the quantity you are trying to find is on its own on the left hand side of the equation,

eg. $\Delta T = \dfrac{E_h}{c\,m}$

☐ 7. Fill in the figures you have, and **write** them down. (You only get marks for what is on paper!)

☐ 8. Do the calculation and write down the answer.

☐ 9. Check that you have included units in your answer and have not written too many figures (see significant figures).

SIGNIFICANT FIGURES

❑   An answer of 3 and 3.0 may appear the same but they mean different things.

Deze   3 means the answer is above 2.5 and below 3.5 (the answer is to 1 significant figure).

3.0 means the answer is above 2.95 and below 3.05 (the answer is to 2 significant figures).

❑   Writing down all the numbers the calculator gives you, eg. 3.0467812, is **wrong** because it claims you know the answer far more accurately than any information you have been given.

❑   In general give answers to **three significant figures** at most.

Round up the next figure.

If the fourth figure is a 5 or above, add one to the third figure.

If the fourth figure is below 5, leave the third figure alone, eg. 3.0467812 becomes 3.05,
                2.9827695 become 2.98.

❑   If using a graph to find information, only use two significant figures.

SCIENTIFIC NOTATION

❑ Many numbers in physics are expressed in scientific notation,
eg. 3×10^8 m s^{-1} is the speed of light.

❑ When written out in full:

1×10^9 = 1 000 000 000
3×10^8 = 300 000 000
5.79×10^7 = 57 900 000

In each case the number of figures, after the first, is given by the value of the indices.

❑ When the indices have a negative value, then the number is less than one.

❑ When written out in full:

1×10^{-3} = 0.001
3×10^{-4} = 0.0003
5.79×10^{-5} = 0.0000579

In each case, the value of the index gives the number of zeros, with the decimal point placed after the first zero.

❑ When putting into calculator:

| 5×10^9 | = | 5 | EXP | 9 | |
| 7×10^{-6} | = | 7 | EXP | 6 | -/+ |

Do not put in the 10 as well.
(EXP is given as EE on some calculators)

❑ **Prefixes** are used with the basic units instead of using scientific notation:

Tera (T)	=	10^{12}	milli (m)	=	10^{-3}
Giga (G)	–	10^9	micro (μ)	=	10^{-6}
Mega (M)	=	10^6	nano (n)	=	10^{-9}
Kilo (k)	=	10^3	pico (p)	=	10^{-12}

❑ All units must be changed to the basic, if given with a prefix.

❑ The only exception is **mass** where the basic unit is the **kg**.

PROPORTIONALITY

❑ Many quantities in physics are **directly proportional** to each other. A certain change in one will always result in exactly the same change in the other.

❑ Direct proportion gives a straight line through the origin on a graph.

❑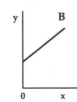

❑ 1. **Graph A**
As **x** varies, so does **y** and the graph formula is **y = mx**, where **m** is the slope or gradient:

$$m = \frac{y_2 - y_1}{x_2 - x_1}$$

❑ 2. **Graph B.**
As **x** varies, so does **y** but when **x = 0**, **y** has a value. The graph formula is **y = mx +c.**
m is still the gradient found as above.
c is the value of **y** when **x = 0**.

❑ 3. **Graph C.**
As **x** increases, **y** decreases.
Since the graph is a curve, it is not easy to see how **x** and **y** are related.
To check, work out **1/x** for each point and replot the points with **y** against **1/x.**
If this gives a straight line through the origin, as shown in **graph D**, then **y** is said to be **indirectly proportional** to **x**.
The graph formula is $y = \frac{m}{x}$.

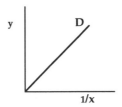

EXPERIMENTAL WRITE-UP FOR LEARNING OUTCOME 3

☐ You have to produce **one** experimental write-up for the course. It can come from any of the individual units. If you are just studying one unit, you must complete an experimental write-up for that unit.

☐ **You must take an active part in the experiment,** helping to carry out the experiment and collecting results.

☐ **You must describe how the experiment is carried out**. This should include:

(1) The aim of the experiment - what you are trying to find out.

(2) A labelled diagram of the apparatus used.

(3) How you changed the independent variable.

(4) What measurements were made, including the apparatus used to do this.

☐ **You must record your results.** This should include:

(1) A clear table of results.

(2) Correct heading for your table, including units.

(3) Results entered in order, either increasing or decreasing values of the independent variable.

☐ **You must analyse your results.** This should include either calculations in a table or a graph:

(a) Appropriate calculations in a table, eg. proving that PV **= a constant**, by calculating the constant for every pair of results.

or

(b) (1) A graph with the dependent and independent variables plotted.

(2) All points accurately plotted.

(3) Axes labelled with both the name of the variable and the units.

(4) A best fit line or curve must be drawn.

❑ **Conclusions must be drawn from the results.**
This should include:

(1) A statement of your conclusion, which must answer the question posed in the aim of the experiment, eg.
aim -   to find the relationship between force and acceleration,
conclusion - the force is directly proportional to the acceleration.

(2) You must state why you have made your conclusion, eg. direct proportion because the graph shows a straight line through the origin.

(3) If you were trying to find the value of a constant, the conclusion must state the value obtained with units.

❑ **You must evaluate your experiment.**
This should include:

(1) The effectiveness of the procedures, ie. did the experiment work well or were there problems in carrying it out.

(2) How you controlled the variables, especially any that had to be kept constant.

(3) Any limitations in the equipment used, eg. meters which only read to one decimal place.

(4) Any possible sources of error.

(5) Any possible improvements you could make to the experiment, perhaps using more accurate equipment or minimising any errors you have identified, eg. heat loss minimised with better insulation.